EASY 4-CHOR
KEYBOARD SONGBOOK
PLAY 21 POPULAR HITS

Published by

Wise Publications
14-15 Berners Street, London, W1T 3LJ, UK.

Exclusive Distributors:

Music Sales Limited
Distribution Centre, Newmarket Road,
Bury St Edmunds, Suffolk, IP33 3YB, UK.

Music Sales Pty Limited
20 Resolution Drive,
Caringbah, NSW 2229, Australia.

Order No. AM993322
ISBN 978-1-84772-505-9
This book © Copyright 2008 Wise Publications,
a division of Music Sales Limited.

Compiled and edited by Jessica Williams.
Music processed by Paul Ewers Music Design Limited.

Printed in the EU.

www.musicsales.com

EASY 4-CHORD KEYBOARD SONGBOOK
PLAY 21 POPULAR HITS

Wise Publications
part of The Music Sales Group
London / New York / Paris / Sydney / Copenhagen / Berlin / Madrid / Tokyo

CONTENTS

BEAUTIFUL DAY

Words by Bono
Music by U2

mov - in' an - y-where. You thought you'd found___ a friend___

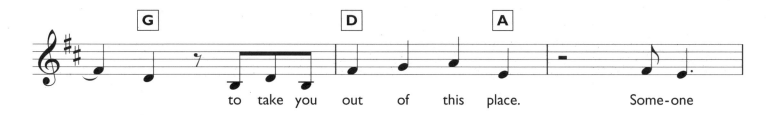

to take you out of this place. Some-one

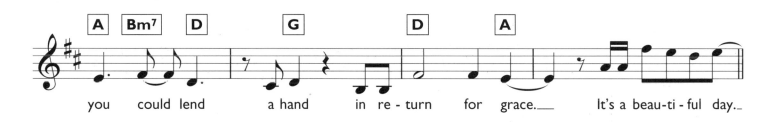

you could lend a hand in re - turn for grace.___ It's a beau-ti - ful day.___

___ Sky falls,___ you feel___

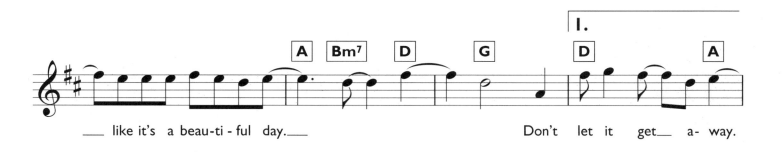

___ like it's a beau-ti - ful day.___ Don't let it get___ a- way.

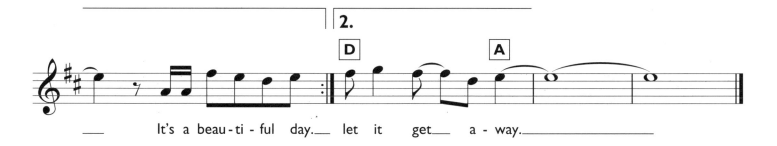

___ It's a beau-ti - ful day.___ let it get___ a - way.___

CIGARETTES & ALCOHOL

Words & Music by Noel Gallagher

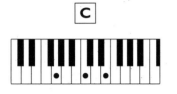
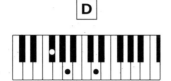

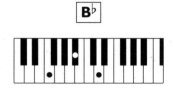

Voice: **Piano**

Rhythm: **Hard Rock**

Tempo: ♩ = 116

Is it my_____ i - ma - gi - na - tion___ or have I

fi - nal - ly found___ some - thing worth liv - ing for?____

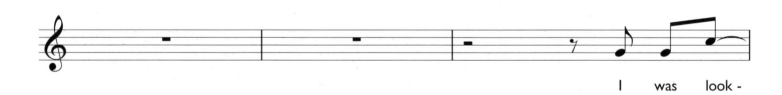

I was look -

- ing for some ac - tion,____ but all____

___ I found___ was cig - ar - ettes and al - co - hol.____

COMMON PEOPLE

Words by Jarvis Cocker

Music by Jarvis Cocker, Nick Banks, Russell Senior, Candida Doyle & Stephen Mackey

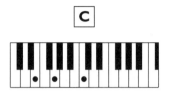
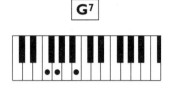

Voice: **Electric Piano**

Rhythm: **Pop Rock**

Tempo: ♩ = 150

She came from Greece, she had a thirst for know - ledge,

she stu - died sculp - ture at St. Mar - tin's col - lege, that's where I___

___ caught her eye.___

She told me that her dad was load - ed,

I said "In that case I'll have rum and Co - ca Co - la." She said "Fine."_

And then in thir - ty se - conds time,___ she said

F

"I want to live like com - mon peo - ple, I want to do what -

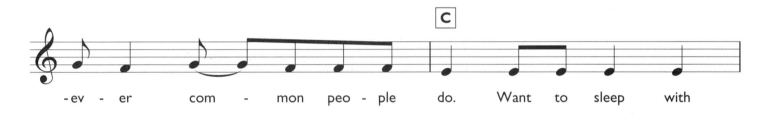

C

-ev - er com - mon peo - ple do. Want to sleep with

com - mon peo - ple, I want to sleep with com-mon peo - ple like you."___

G⁷

___ Well what else___ could I do?___ I said I'll...

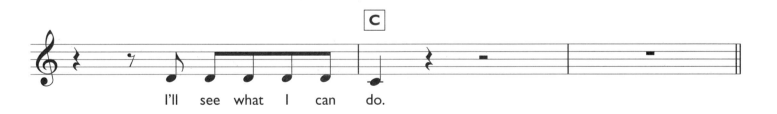

C

I'll see what I can do.

Repeat to fade

Want to live like com - mon peo - ple like you.

DREAMS

Words by Dolores O'Riordan
Music by Dolores O'Riordan & Noel Hogan

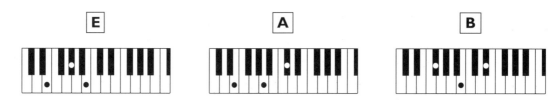

Voice: **Vocal Aahs**

Rhythm: **Dance Pop**

Tempo: ♩ = 126

Oh, my life is

chang - ing e - ve - ry - day,_____ in

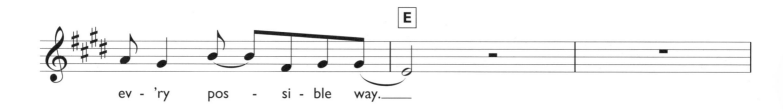

ev - 'ry pos - si - ble way._____

And oh, my dreams, it's

ne - ver quite____ as it seems,_____ it's

ne - ver quite__ as it seems.__

I know I've felt___ like this___ be - fore,__

__ but now I'm feel - ing it ev - en more,__

__ be - cause it came__ from you.__

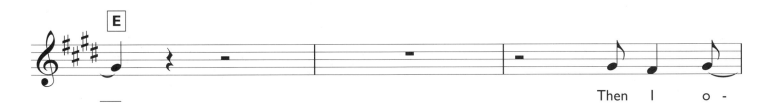

__ Then I o -

- pen up__ and see__ the per - son fall - ing here__ is me,__

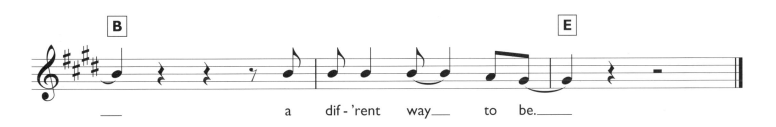

__ a dif - 'rent way__ to be.__

FIELDS OF GOLD

Words & Music by Sting

Bm 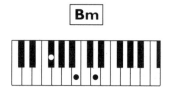 **G** 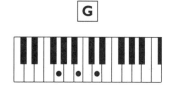 **D** 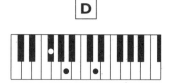 **A**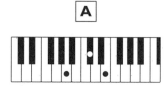

Voice: **Clarinet**

Rhythm: **Soft Rock**

Tempo: ♩ = 96

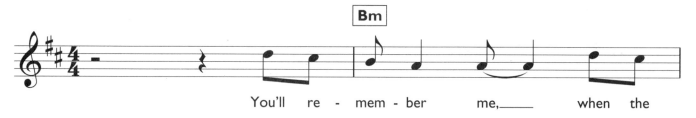

You'll re - mem - ber me,___ when the

west wind moves,___ up - on the fields___ of bar -

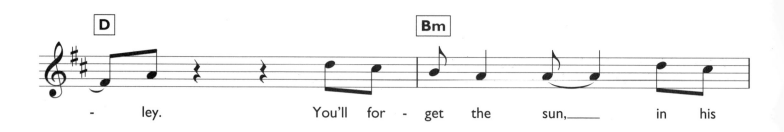

- ley. You'll for - get the sun,___ in his

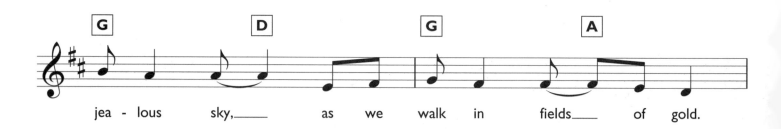

jea - lous sky,___ as we walk in fields___ of gold.

HAVE A NICE DAY

Words & Music by Kelly Jones

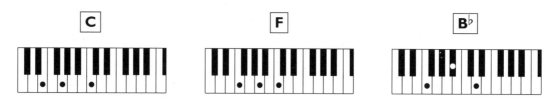

Voice: **Honky Tonk Piano**

Rhythm: **Lite Pop**

Tempo: ♩ = 120

San Fran - cis - co Bay, past pier thir - ty nine,

ear - ly P. M., can't___ re - mem - ber what time.___

Got the wait - ing cab, stopped at the red light,

ad - dress we're sure___ of, but it's turned out just right.

HEY YA!

Words & Music by André Benjamin

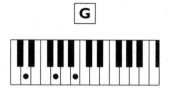
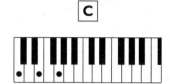
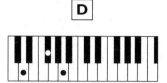
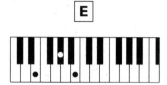

Voice: **Clarinet**

Rhythm: **Pop Rock**

Tempo: ♩ = 144

My ba-by don't mess a-round_ be-cause she loves me so__ and this I

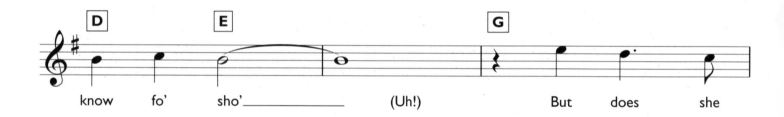

know fo' sho'_____ (Uh!) But does she

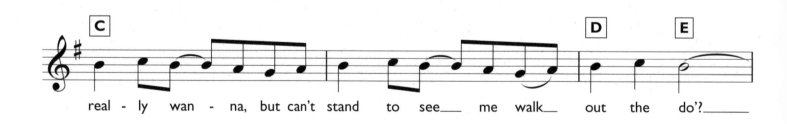

real-ly wan-na, but can't stand to see__ me walk__ out the do'?_____

_ Don't try to fight the feel-ing 'cos the

HIT THE ROAD JACK

Words & Music by Percy Mayfield

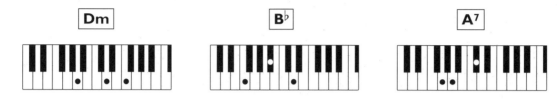

Voice: **Trumpet**

Rhythm: **Swing**

Tempo: ♩ = 168

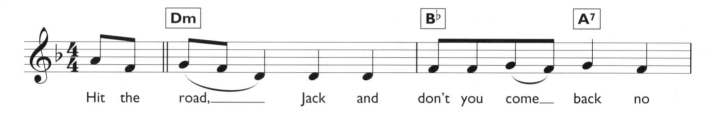

Hit the road,_____ Jack and don't you come__ back no

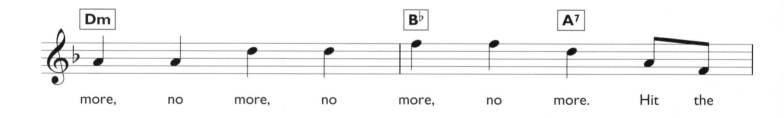

more, no more, no more, no more. Hit the

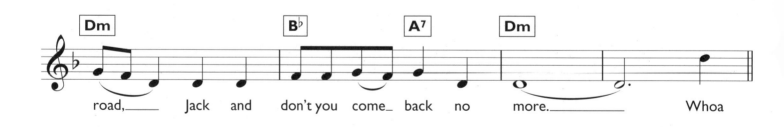

road,_____ Jack and don't you come__ back no more._____ Whoa

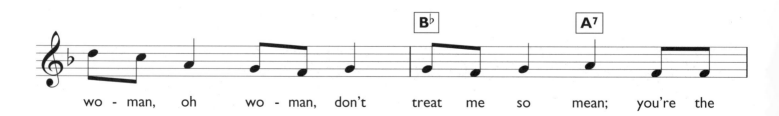

wo - man, oh wo - man, don't treat me so mean; you're the

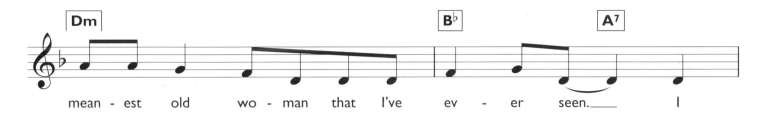

mean - est old wo - man that I've ev - er seen.____ I

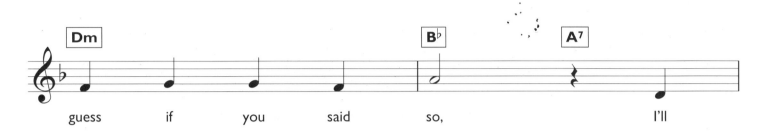

guess if you said so, I'll

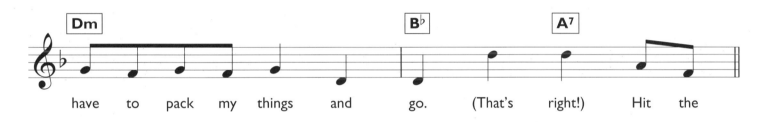

have to pack my things and go. (That's right!) Hit the

road,_____ Jack and don't you come____ back no

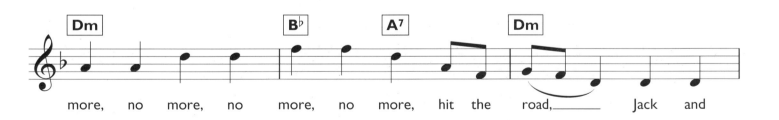

more, no more, no more, no more, hit the road,_____ Jack and

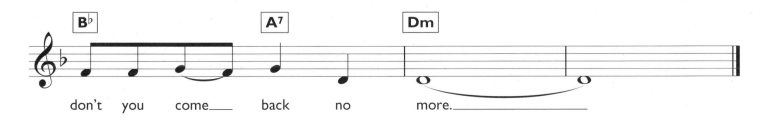

don't you come____ back no more._____

HOUND DOG

Words & Music by Jerry Leiber & Mike Stoller

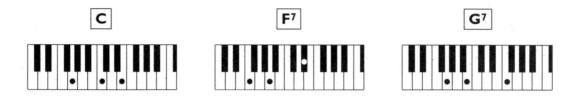

Voice: **Electric Organ 2**

Rhythm: **50s Rock**

Tempo: ♩ = 144

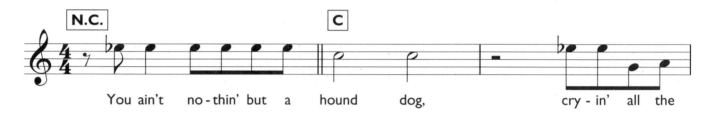

You ain't no-thin' but a hound dog, cry-in' all the

time. You ain't no-thin' but a hound dog,

cry-in' all the time. Well___ you ain't

nev - er caught a rab-bit and you ain't no friend___ of

mine. When they said you was

high - classed, well that was just a lie.

When they said you was high - classed, well that was just a

lie. Well___ you ain't nev - er caught a rab - bit and you

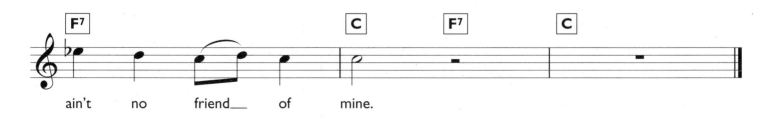

ain't no friend___ of mine.

I HAVE A DREAM

Words & Music by Benny Andersson & Björn Ulvaeus

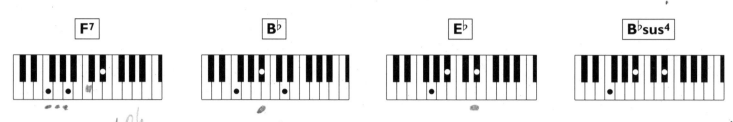

F⁷   **B♭**   **E♭**   **B♭sus⁴**

Voice: **Bass/Piano Split**

Rhythm: **Soul Ballad**

Tempo: ♩ = 112

I have a dream, a song to sing to help me

cope with a - ny - thing. If you see the

won - der of a fai - ry tale, you can take the

fu - ture ev - en if you fail. I be - lieve in

an - gels,   some-thing good in ev - 'ry - thing I

see,   I be - lieve in an - gels,   when I know the

time is right for me, I'll cross the stream,   I have a

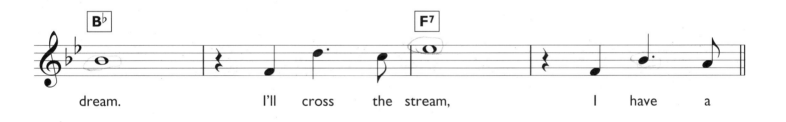

dream.   I'll cross the stream,   I have a

dream.

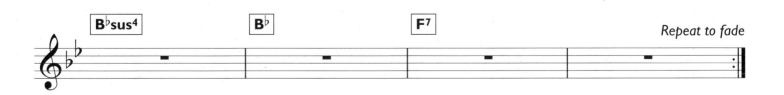

Repeat to fade

IS IT ANY WONDER?

Words & Music by Richard Hughes, James Sanger, Tim Rice-Oxley & Tom Chaplin

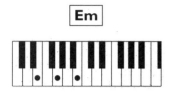 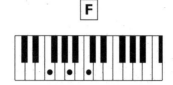 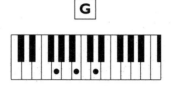 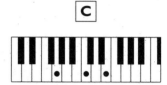

Voice: **Electric Guitar**

Rhythm: **Hard Rock**

Tempo: ♩ = 128

I, I al-ways thought that I knew I'd

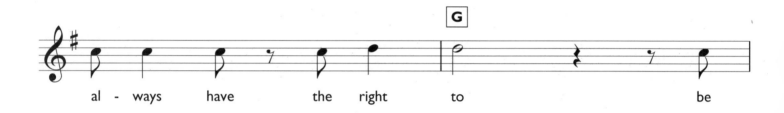

al - ways have the right to be

liv-ing in the king-dom of the good___ and true___

___ and so on. But now I think I was

wrong and you were laugh-ing a - long, and

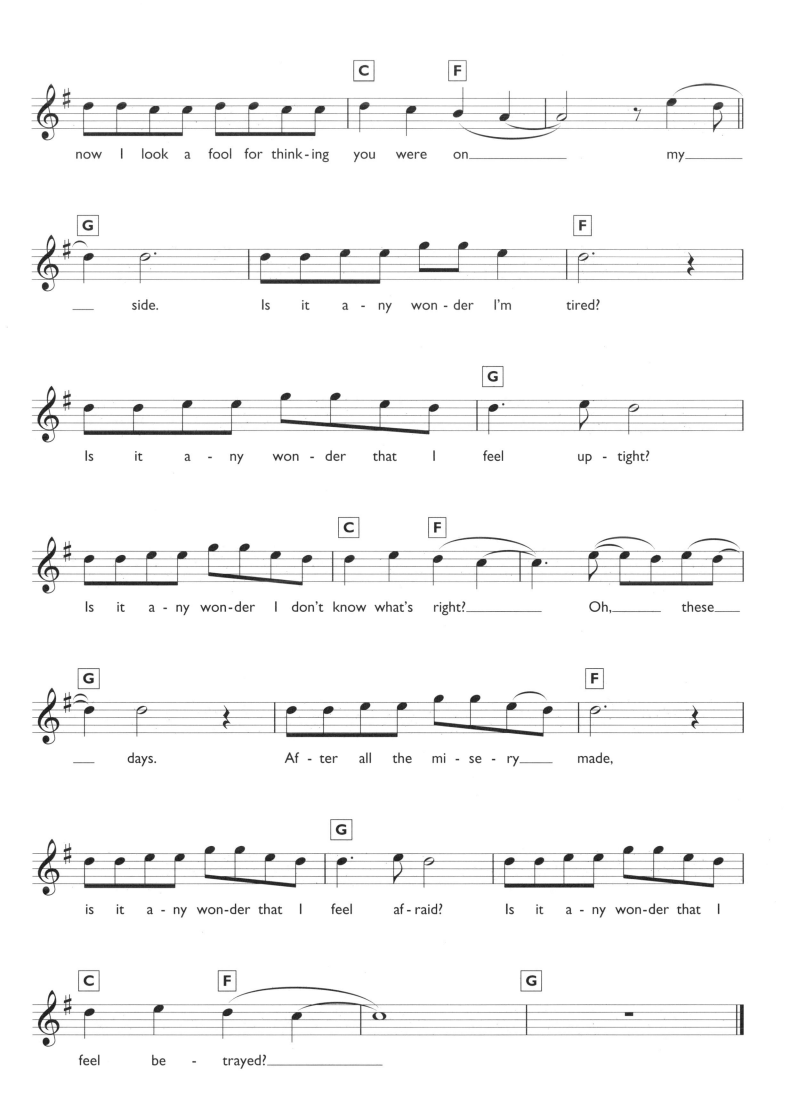

JOLENE

Words & Music by Dolly Parton

Voice: **Acoustic Guitar**

Rhythm: **Country**

Tempo: ♩ = 108

Jo - lene, Jo - lene, Jo - lene, Jo - lene,_____ I'm

beg-ging of you, please don't take my man._____ Jo - lene, Jo - lene, Jo-

-lene, Jo - lene,_____ please don't take him just be-cause_ you

can._____ Your beau-ty is be - yond com-pare, with

flam-ing locks of au-burn hair, with iv-'ry skin and eyes of em - 'rald

green._____ Your smile is like a breath of spring, your voice is soft like

28

LOVE ME DO

Words & Music by John Lennon & Paul McCartney

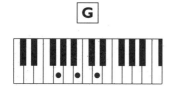
G

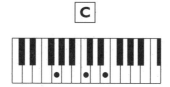
C

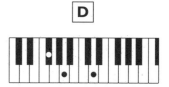
D

Voice: **Electric Guitar**

Rhythm: **4 Beat Rock**

Tempo: ♩ = 138

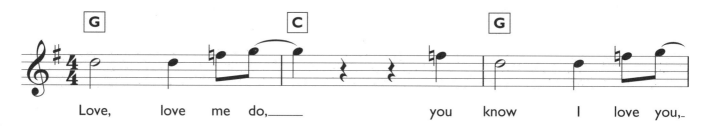

Love, love me do,____ you know I love you,_

_ I'll al - ways be true,____ so

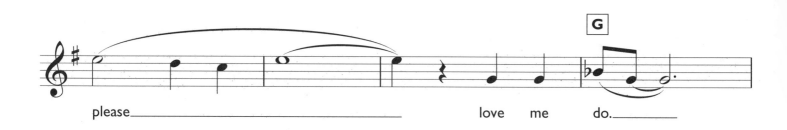

please_____ love me do._____

love____ me do.____

MILLENNIUM

Words & Music by Robbie Williams, John Barry, Leslie Bricusse & Guy Chambers

Voice: **Soprano Saxophone**

Rhythm: **Pop Ballad**

Tempo: ♩ = 84

Some say that we are play-ers, some

say that we are pawns,_ but we've been mak-ing mo-ney since_ the day_

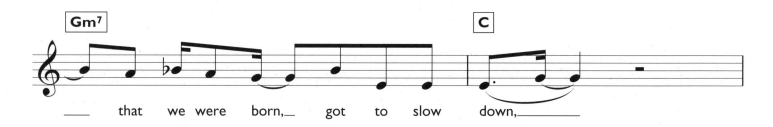

____ that we were born,_ got to slow down,_____

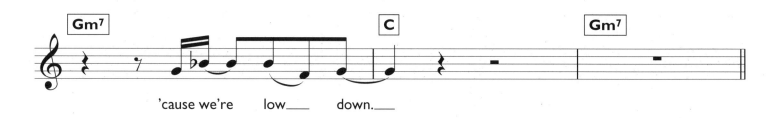

'cause we're low___ down.___

Run a-round in cir-cles, live a life___ of so-li-tude,_ till we find_

MR. TAMBOURINE MAN

Words & Music by Bob Dylan

Voice: **Electric Piano**

Rhythm: **Bossa Nova**

Tempo: ♩ = 138

PLAY DEAD

Words & Music by David Arnold, Björk Gudmundsdottir & John Wardle

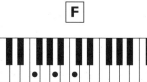

Voice: **Trumpet**

Rhythm: **Industrial Rock**

Tempo: ♩ = 78

Dar - ling,___ stop__ con - fus - ing__ me ___

___ with your wish - ful__ think - ing. Hope - ful___

em - bra - ces,___ don't you un - der - stand?

I have to__ go through__ this,___

I be - long to here where no - one cares and no - one loves.___

No light no air to live in, a place called hate, the ci-ty of fear.

(vocal ad lib.)

I play dead, it stops the hurt-ing. I play dead and the hurt stops.

ROCKIN' ALL OVER THE WORLD

Words & Music by John Fogerty

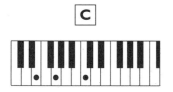
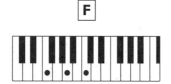

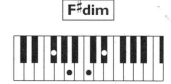

Voice: **Distortion Guitar**

Rhythm: **4 Beat Rock**

Tempo: ♩ = 132

A' here we are,_ here we are and here we go,_ all a - board_ and we're

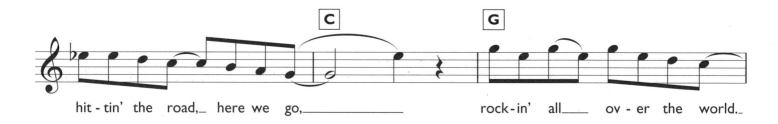

hit - tin' the road,_ here we go,_____ rock-in' all___ ov - er the world._

_ A' gid - dy up,_ gid - dy up and

get a - way,_ we're go - in' cra - zy and we're go - in' to - day,_ here we go,

_____ rock-in' all___ ov - er the world._ And I like_

THE SCIENTIST

Words & Music by Guy Berryman, Chris Martin, Jon Buckland & Will Champion

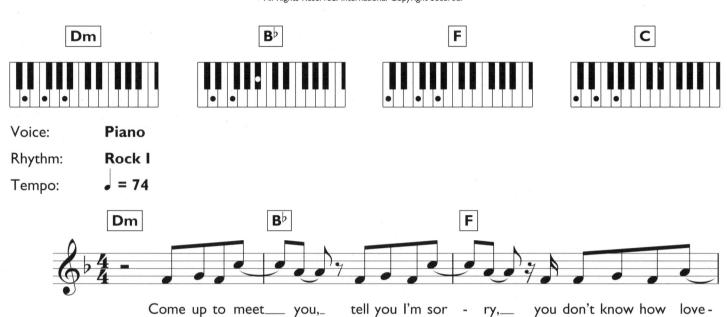

Voice: **Piano**

Rhythm: **Rock I**

Tempo: ♩ = 74

Come up to meet___ you,___ tell you I'm sor - ry,___ you don't know how love-

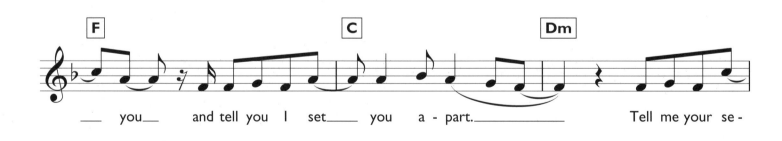

- ly you are._____ I had to find___ you,___ tell you I need___

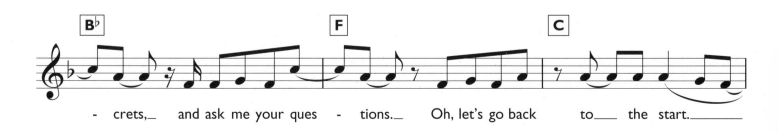

___ you___ and tell you I set___ you a - part._____ Tell me your se-

- crets,___ and ask me your ques - tions.___ Oh, let's go back to___ the start._____

SONGBIRD

Words & Music by Liam Gallagher

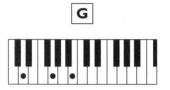  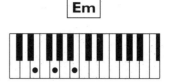 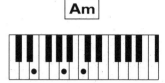

Voice: **Piano**

Rhythm: **Skiffle Rock**

Tempo: ♩ = 138

Talk-ing to the song-bird yes-ter-day___ flew me to a place not far a-

-way. She's a lit-tle pi-lot in my mind, sing-ing songs of love to pass the time.___

_____ Gon-na write a song so she can see, give her all the love she gives to

me. Talk of bet-ter days that have yet to come, I've ne-ver felt this love from a-ny-one.___

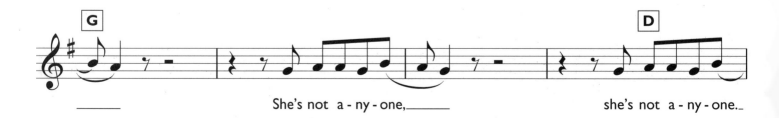

_____ She's not a-ny-one,_____ she's not a-ny-one._

She's not a - ny - one.

A man can ne-ver dream these kind of things_ es-pec-ial-ly when she came and spread her

wings. Whis-pered in my ear the things I'd like then she flew a - way in - to the night._

_____ Gon-na write a song so she can see, give her all the love she gives to

me. Talk of bet-ter days that have yet to come ne-ver felt this love from a - ny - one._

_____ She's not a - ny - one,_____ she's not a - ny - one._

She's not a - ny - one._

THE SOUND OF SILENCE

Words & Music by Paul Simon

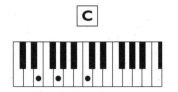
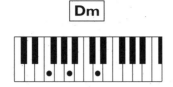
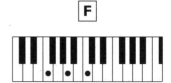
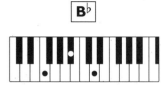

Voice: **Acoustic Guitar**

Rhythm: **Rock**

Tempo: ♩ = 108

Hel - lo dark-ness my old friend, I've come to talk with you a -

-gain. Be - cause a vi - sion soft - ly creep - ing,

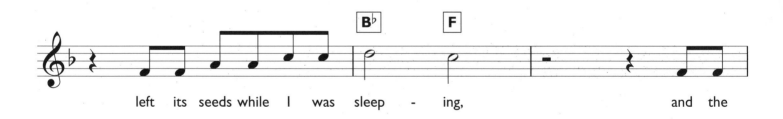

left its seeds while I was sleep - ing, and the

vi - sion_____ that was plant-ed in my brain still re - mains

with-in the sound of si - lence.__ In rest-less dreams I walked a -

-lone, nar - row streets of cob - ble - stone,

'neath the ha - lo of a street - lamp,__ I turned my col - lar to the

cold and damp,__ when my eyes were stabbed_ by the

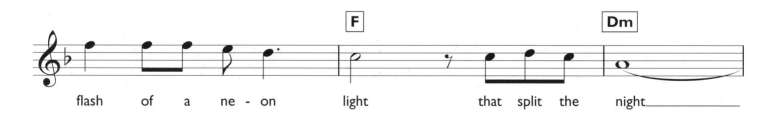

flash of a ne - on light that split the night____

___ and touched the sound of si - lence.____

YOU'RE GORGEOUS

Words & Music by Stephen Jones

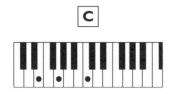 C 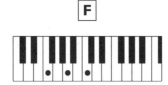 F 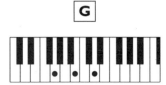 G

Voice: **Marimba**

Rhythm: **Reggae 16**

Tempo: = 126

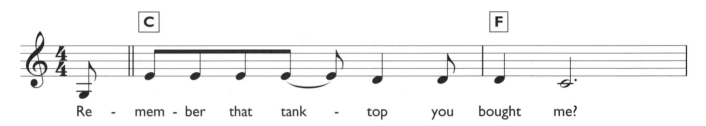

Re - mem - ber that tank - top you bought me?

You wrote___ "You're gor - geous" on it.___

You took me to your rent - ed mo - tor car,

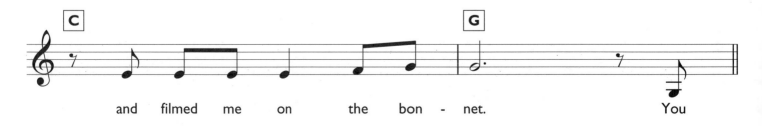

and filmed me on the bon - net. You

got me to hitch___ my knees up, and pull___ my

legs___ a - part.___ You took an in - sta - ma - tic ca - me - ra,

and pulled my sleeves a - round___ my heart. Be - cause

you're___ gor - geous I'd do a - ny - thing___ for you.___

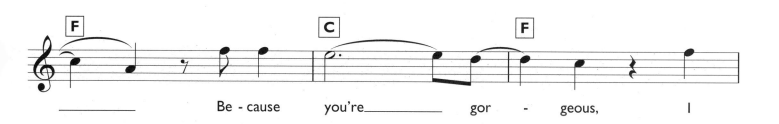

___ Be - cause you're___ gor - geous, I

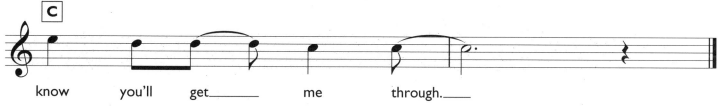

know you'll get___ me through.___